Flute part   Chris Graham

the best of grade
Flute

A compilation of the best Grade 2 flute pieces ever selected by the major examination boards

Selected and edited by Sally Adams

To buy Faber Music publications or to find out about the full range of titles available
please contact your local music retailer or Faber Music sales enquiries:

Faber Music Limited, Burnt Mill, Elizabeth Way, Harlow CM20 2HX
Tel: +44 (0)1279 82 89 82   Fax: +44 (0)1279 82 89 83
sales@fabermusic.com   fabermusic.com

Contents

The performers

Sally Adams is a player and teacher of many years' experience. She is author of the successful *Flute Basics* method and various other flute repertoire volumes.

Robin Bigwood is a freelance pianist and harpsichordist, performing with Passacaglia, Feinstein Ensemble, Britten Sinfonia and as a soloist. He also works as a sound engineer and producer.

Philippa Davies (track 8) is an international soloist with many orchestras, plays chamber music with the Nash Ensemble and London Winds and has many recordings to her name.

Track 1: Tuning note A

© 2010 by Faber Music Ltd
This edition first published in 2010
Bloomsbury House 74–77 Great Russell Street London WC1B 3DA
Music processed by Jackie Leigh
Design by Økvik Design
Printed in England by Caligraving Ltd
All rights reserved

ISBN10: 0-571-53070-2
EAN13: 978-0-571-53070-0

All audio tracks recorded in Priors Marston, July 2009
Performed by Sally Adams (Flute) and Robin Bigwood (Piano)
(with the exception of Track 8 performed by Philippa Davies)

Engineered by Robin Bigwood; Produced by Leigh Rumsey
℗ 2010 Faber Music Ltd © 2010 Faber Music Ltd

Hungarian fantaisie

from 'First Repertoire for Flute'

PERFORMANCE 2
ACCOMPANIMENT 3

This piece should have a mournful and yearning quality. The moods change subtly throughout.
Use the dynamic and articulation contrasts to express these moods effectively.

Karl Joachim Andersen (1847–1909)

arr. Sally Adams

Tambourin

from 'Flute All Sorts'

PERFORMANCE 4
ACCOMPANIMENT 5

Keep the mood of the major section light and sunny. Think about how to use
articulation to achieve this and follow the dynamic contrasts carefully.

Giovanni Battista Somis (1686–1763)

arr. Harris/Adams

What shall we do with the drunken sailor?

from 'What Else Can I Play? Grade 2'

PERFORMANCE 6
ACCOMPANIMENT 7

Make sure that the repeated rhythm pattern in bar 3 etc. is always light and clearly defined.
Perhaps experiment with double-tonguing to achieve this effect.

Traditional

Oh soldier, soldier

from 'Going Solo'

PERFORMANCE 8
ACCOMPANIMENT 9

Feel the marching rhythm set up in the piano, play the notes short, and look at the dynamics:
crescendo to *forte* and then end quietly as if the soldiers are marching towards you and away again.

Traditional
arr. Paul Reade

Barcarolle

from 'Flute All Sorts'

PERFORMANCE
ACCOMPANIMENT

Try to create a sense of wistful sadness in this piece. Work on producing a beautiful tone and play right through the phrases. Make sure you always use the correct fingering for middle E♭.

Pyotr Ilyich Tchaikovsky (1840–1893)

arr. Harris/Adams

Cat walk

from 'Really Easy Jazzin' About'

PERFORMANCE 12
ACCOMPANIMENT 13

This piece should have a confident and unhurried swagger. Experiment with a different articulation syllable in the first bar – perhaps try 'do-da-do-dhaa'. Make the phrases from bar 11 to 18 really *cantabile*.

With a good swing ♩ = 112

Pam Wedgwood (b.1947)

Jig along

from 'Step It Up!'

PERFORMANCE 14
ACCOMPANIMENT 15

Give this piece a cheeky, dance-like feel. There are lots of different dynamic markings throughout. Can you make a difference between *mp* and *p*, for example?

Louise Chamberlain (b.1947)

Sea chant

from 'Two Easy Pieces'

This piece should have a gentle ebb and flow; keep your articulation soft and gentle to achieve this.
Count the tied notes carefully. Perhaps add some dynamics of your own to give the phrases shape.

Peter Sculthorpe (b.1929)

Mai

from 'Woodwind World Book 2'

PERFORMANCE 18
ACCOMPANIMENT 19

This piece requires a warm cantabile tone. Make sure that you play right through the dotted minims. Observe the tempo changes carefully.

Gabriel Fauré (1845–1924)

arr. Harrison

Piece No.3

from '14 pièces pour flûte et piano'

PERFORMANCE 20
ACCOMPANIMENT 21

This piece needs a dark and mysterious yet always *cantabile* tone. Make sure that your finger movements are absolutely smooth on the wider intervals. How softly can you play the last note?

Charles Koechlin (1867–1950)

Hessian dance

from '76 Graded Studies for Flute'

This study needs lots of bounce and energy in the articulation to create a dance-like feel.
Try to create a sense of one in a bar.

PERFORMANCE 22

Anon.

Study No.14

from '76 Graded Studies for Flute'

PERFORMANCE 23

Make sure that you have the tempo of this study firmly established in your head before you start to play.
Be aware of the articulation and dynamic contrasts and how they shape the character of the piece.

Allegro ♩ = 126

Carl Baermann (1810–1885)

The sun from the East

from '76 Graded Studies for Flute'

PERFORMANCE 24

This piece should have a confident and purposeful feel. Keep the tone bright and warm throughout.
Make sure the fingerwork is fluent and even when you play the slurred quavers.

Anon.

Study No.40

from 'Jazz Flute Studies'

This study should have a very easy yet sophisticated feel. Look carefully at the rhythm
and articulation in bar 2 and don't shorten the long notes at the ends of phrases.

James Rae (b.1957)

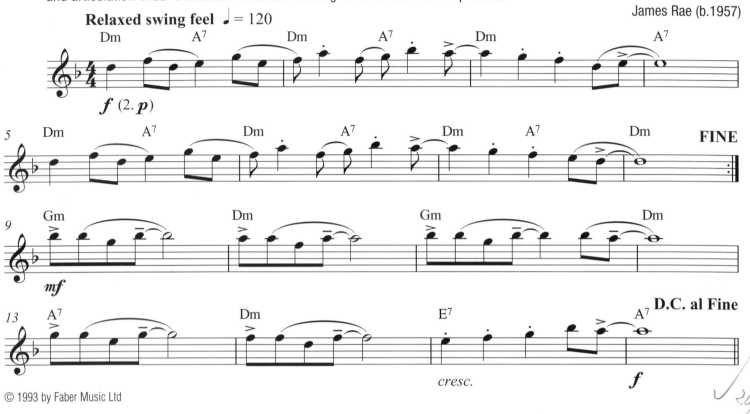

LIST C (Trinity Guildhall 2007–11)

Old Japanese folk song

from 'Flute All Sorts'

Create a mood of calm yet deep sadness in this piece; imagine you are telling a story and allow the music to
unfold gently. Count the long notes and rests carefully. Experiment with a 'hollow' tone in the quieter phrases.

Traditional
arr. Harris/Adams

Galloping galoshes

PERFORMANCE 27

from 'Improve Your Scales! Grades 1-3'

Include some *crescendos* and *diminuendos* to give more movement and dynamic interest
to the phrases. Try playing the notes in bars 4–7 a little lighter to give more contrast.

Paul Harris

Arabian apricot

PERFORMANCE 28

from 'Improve Your Scales! Grades 1-3'

In which key is this piece written? Practise the scale carefully. Listen to your *legato* –
do the notes join up really smoothly? Try to make the various dynamic levels really contrasted.

Paul Harris

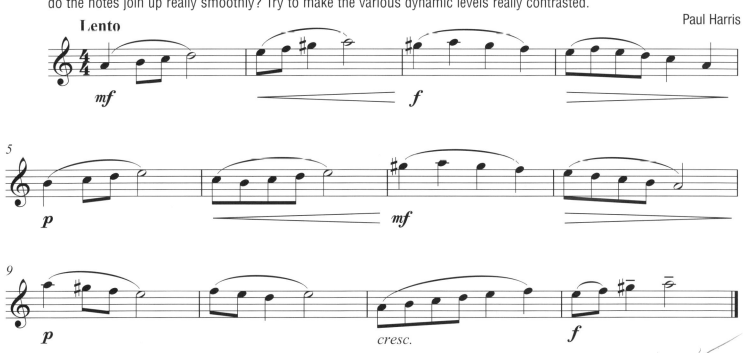

Hallelujah!

from 'Flute All Sorts'

PERFORMANCE

This piece should sparkle with energy and joy. Exaggerate the articulation to make the most of the syncopated rhythms. Never let the tempo drop, particularly in the quieter phrases.

Pam Wedgwood (b.1947)